For Ben — Teresa Heapy

For my father, whose childhood adventures
helped inspire these drawings — Katie Cleminson

LOVED TO BITS
is a DAVID FICKLING BOOK
First published in Great Britain in 2018 by
David Fickling Books,
31 Beaumont Street,
Oxford, OX1 2NP

www.davidficklingbooks.com

Text © Teresa Heapy, 2018
Illustrations © Katie Cleminson, 2018

978-1-910200-63-6

1 3 5 7 9 10 8 6 4 2

WARNING: This book will make you LOVE YOUR BEAR!

Papers used by David Fickling Books are from well-managed forests and other responsible sources.

DAVID FICKLING BOOKS Reg. No. 8340307

A CIP catalogue record for this book is available from the British Library.

Printed and bound in China by Toppan Leefung

Designed by Ness Wood
Edited by Alice Corrie

LOVED

TO BITS

Teresa Heapy & Katie Cleminson

David Fickling Books

My ted's special.
Stripy Ted.

He's not allowed
to leave my bed.

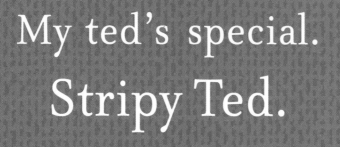

For long ago, he was . . .

. . . a super, somersaulting ted,

all golden stripes
from foot to head,

who made adventures
round my bed
from dreams we had,
and books we read.

We foiled the plot,

we fought the beast,

we rode,

we hid, we found the feast.

We tickled
monsters,

fled on rafts,

we searched,

explored,

escaped . . .

and laughed.

And if I stumbled,
back he sped
to rescue me,
with arms outspread.

"Take my paw . . .

and
ONWARDS!"

said my furry,
funny, fearless ted.

And then the time his eye went

PING!

"It's nothing! Didn't feel a thing!"

And once, within a tug-of-war . . .

And once, his leg got tangled,

. . . thump!

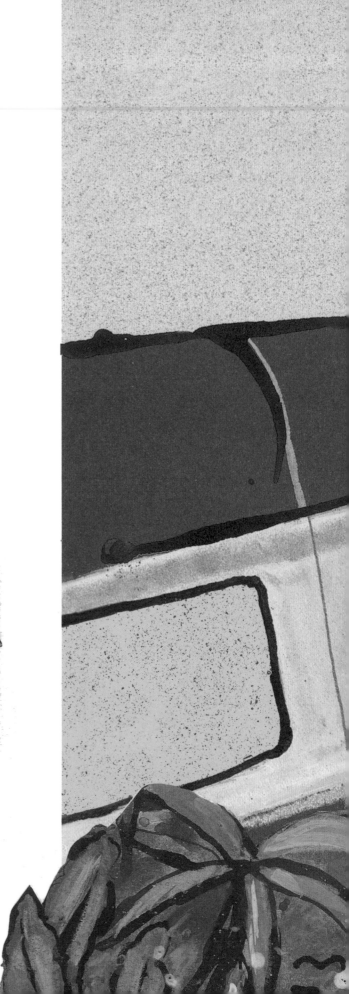

he slipped.

I caught
his paw.

I held him
tightly

just

once

more.

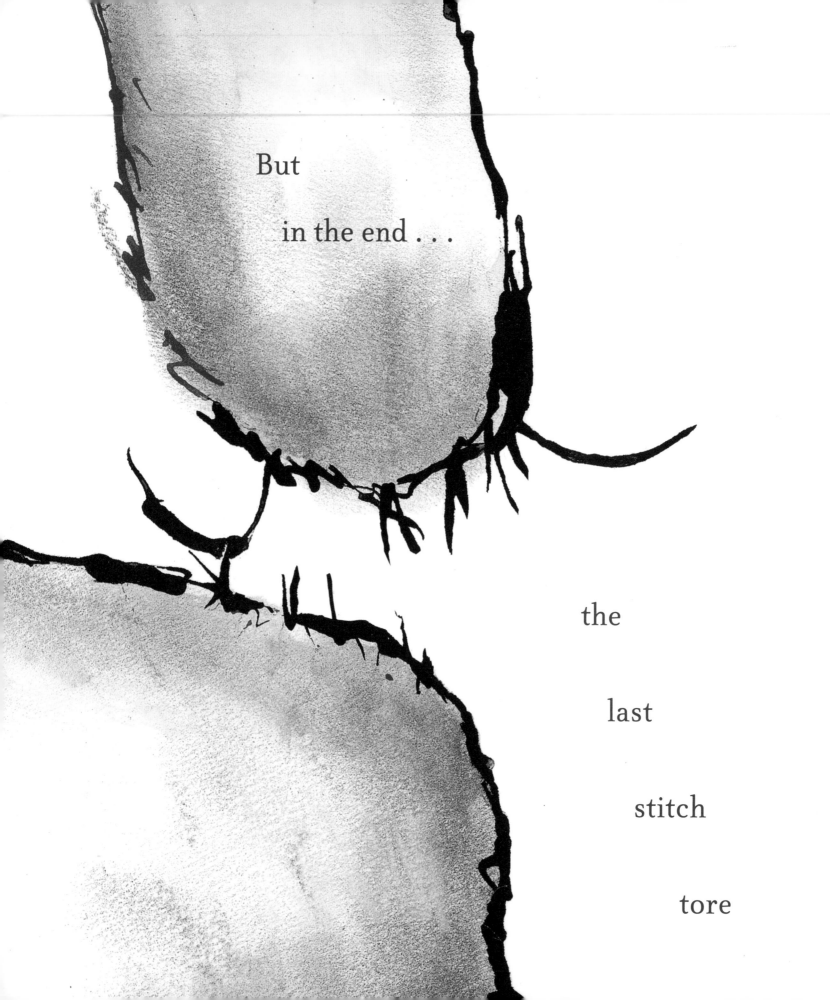

But

in the end . . .

the

last

stitch

tore

and

Stripy Ted

fell

to

the

floor.

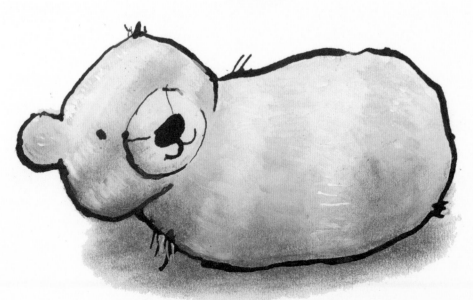

I picked him up.

A scruffy ted.

No arms and legs –
just hanging threads.

Stripes loved off,
all brown instead.

Battered,

worn-out

ball and head.

Mum reached for him.

"Poor little ted.
Shall I mend him?"

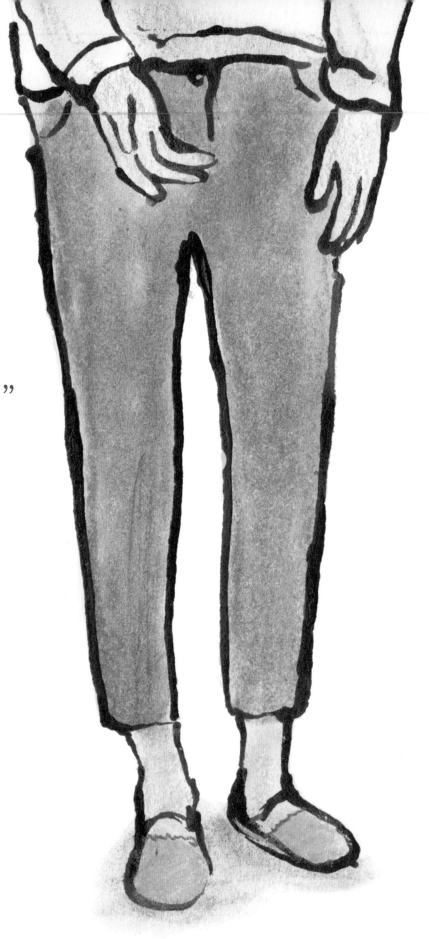

"No," I said.

The truth
was now,

I liked him better.

I could hold him in one hand.

He fitted right,

just here.

He knows my hopes,
my secret schemes,

my stories,
wishes,
fears and
dreams.

Yes, my ted's special.
Stripy Ted.

And he belongs with me in bed.